ISADOR A. INCHWORM'S

BOOK OF MATH TALES

The Good Time Mathematics Storybook

Good Time Mathematics
developed by
The Amazing Life Games Company
for Holt, Rinehart and Winston, Inc.

ISBN 0-03-091542-2
2345678901   122   987654321

What about this book?

IF YOU LIKE TO FIND OUT THINGS FOR YOURSELF, THEN YOU SHOULD READ THIS BOOK.

IT'S NOT IN ANY SPECIAL ORDER, SO YOU CAN READ ANY PART OF IT WHENEVER YOU WANT.

IT MIGHT NOT ALWAYS LOOK LIKE IT, BUT EVERYTHING INSIDE IS ABOUT MATH. MAYBE THERE'S A STORY OR SOMETHING THAT WILL HELP YOU SEE YOUR WORLD IN A NEW WAY.

HERE'S WHAT'S INSIDE

B.C.
Johnny Hart

Euclid

Vachel Lindsay

Old Euclid drew a circle
On a sand-beach long ago.
He bounded and enclosed it
With angles thus and so.
His set of solemn graybeards
Nodded and argued much
Of arc and of circumference,
Diameters and such.
A silent child stood by them
From morning until noon
Because they drew such charming
Round pictures of the moon.

Arithmetic

Carl Sandburg

Arithmetic is where numbers fly like pigeons in and out of your head.

Arithmetic tells you how many you lose or win if you know how many you had before you lost or won.

Arithmetic is seven eleven all good children go to heaven—or five six bundle of sticks.

Arithmetic is numbers you squeeze from your head to your hand to your pencil to your paper till you get the answer.

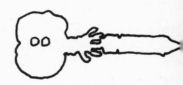

Arithmetic is where the answer is right and everything is nice and you can look out of the window and see the blue sky—or the answer is wrong and you have to start all over and try again and see how it comes out this time.

8

If you take a number and double it and double it again and then double it a few more times, the number gets bigger and bigger and goes higher and higher and only arithmetic can tell you what the number is when you decide to quit doubling.

Arithmetic is where you have to multiply —and you carry the multiplication table in your head and hope you won't lose it.

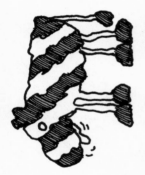

If you have two animal crackers, one good and one bad, and you eat one and a striped zebra with streaks all over him eats the other, how many animal crackers will you have if somebody offers you five six seven and you say No no no and you say Nay nay nay and you say Nix nix nix?

If you ask your mother for one fried egg for breakfast and she gives you two fried eggs and you eat both of them, who is better in arithmetic, you or your mother?

9

Paul Bunyan
versus the Conveyor Belt

William Hazlett Upson

One of Paul Bunyan's most brilliant successes came about, not because of brilliant thinking, but because of Paul's caution and carefulness. This was the famous affair of the conveyor belt.

Paul and his mechanic, Ford Fordsen, had started to work a uranium mine in Colorado. The ore was brought out on an endless belt which ran half a mile going into the mine and another half mile coming out—giving it a total length of one mile. It was four feet wide. It ran on a series of rollers and was driven by a pulley mounted on the transmission of Paul's big blue truck, "Babe." The manufacturers of the belt had made it all in one piece, without any splice or lacing, and they had put a half-twist in the return part so that the wear would be the same on both sides.

After several months' operation the mine gallery had become twice as long, but the amount of material coming out was less. Paul decided he needed a belt twice as long and half as wide. He told Ford Fordsen to take his chain saw and cut the belt in two lengthwise.

11

"That will give us two belts," said Ford Fordsen. "We'll have to cut them in two crosswise and splice them together. That means I'll have to go to town and buy the materials for two splices."

"No," said Paul. "This belt has a half-twist—which makes it what is known in geometry as a Moebius strip."

"What difference does that make?" asked Ford Fordsen.

"A Moebius strip," said Paul Bunyan, "has only one side, and one edge, and if we cut it in two lengthwise, it will still be in one piece. We'll have one belt twice as long and half as wide."

"How can you cut something in two and have it still in one piece?" asked Ford Fordsen.

Paul was modest. He was never opinionated. "Let's try this thing out," he said.

They went into Paul's office. Paul took a strip of gummed paper about two inches wide and a yard long. He laid it on his desk with the gummed side up. He lifted the two ends and brought them together in front of him with the gummed sides down. Then he turned one of the ends over, licked it, slid it under the other end, and stuck the two gummed sides together. He had made himself an endless paper belt with a half-twist in it just like the big belt on the conveyor.

"This," said Paul, "is a Moebius strip. It will perform just the way I said—I hope."

Paul took a pair of scissors, dug the point in the center of the paper, and cut the paper strip in two lengthwise. And when he had finished, sure enough, he had one strip twice as long, half as wide, and with a double twist in it.

Ford Fordsen was convinced. He went out and started cutting the big belt in two. And, at this point, a man called Loud Mouth Johnson arrived to see how Paul's enterprise was coming along and to offer any destructive criticism that might occur to him. Loud Mouth Johnson, being Public Blow-Hard Number One, found plenty to find fault with.

"If you cut that belt in two lengthwise, you will end up with two belts, each the same length as the original belt, but only half as wide."

"No," said Ford Fordsen, "this is a very special belt known as a Moebius strip. If I cut it in two lengthwise, I will end up with one belt twice as long and half as wide."

"Want to bet?" said Loud Mouth Johnson.

"Sure," said Ford Fordsen.

They bet a thousand dollars. And, of course, Ford Fordsen won. Loud Mouth Johnson was so astounded that he slunk off and stayed away for six months. When he finally came back he found Paul Bunyan just starting to cut the belt in two lengthwise for the second time.

"What's the idea?" asked Loud Mouth Johnson.

Paul Bunyan said, "The tunnel has progressed much farther and the material coming out is not as bulky as it was. So I am lengthening the belt again and making it narrower."

"Where is Ford Fordsen?"

Paul Bunyan said, "I have sent him to town to get some materials to splice the belt. When I get through cutting it in two lengthwise I will have two belts of the same length but only half the width of this one. So I will have to do some splicing."

Loud Mouth Johnson could hardly believe his ears. Here was a chance to get his thousand dollars back and show up Paul Bunyan as a boob besides. "Listen," said Loud Mouth Johnson, "when you get through you will have only one belt twice as long and half as wide."

"Want to bet?"

"Sure."

So they bet a thousand dollars and, of course, Loud Mouth Johnson lost again. It wasn't so much that Paul Bunyan was brilliant. It was just that he was methodical. He had tried it out with that strip of gummed paper, and he knew that the second time you slice a Moebius strip you get two pieces—linked together like an old-fashioned watch chain.

A mathematician confided
That a Moebius band is one-sided.
And you'll get quite a laugh
If you cut one in half,
For it stays in one piece when divided.

Ripley's ⟶ Believe It or Not!

Ripley's Believe-it-or-Not is a newspaper cartoon that tells odd facts about the world. Here are some of the strange things Ripley found out about numbers.

BEES
GATHERING ONE POUND OF HONEY FLY A DISTANCE EQUIVALENT TO *TWICE AROUND THE EARTH*

EMPEROR JAHANGIR
(1567-1627) Mogul ruler of Hindustan
CELEBRATED HIS 48th BIRTHDAY BY GIVING THE HIGHBORN BRAHMANS IN HIS EMPIRE 9 GIFTS

-HIS WEIGHT IN PRECIOUS STONES, IN GOLD, IN SILVER, IN GOLD CLOTH, IN COTTON GOODS, IN SPICES, IN FLOUR, IN BUTTER AND IN CORN (Sept. 1, 1617)

THE MOSQUE OF SULTAN SELIM II
in Adrianople, Turkey,
DESIGNED BY AN ADMIRER OF THE ARABIAN NIGHTS, WAS BUILT **WITH 999 WINDOWS-**

THE ARABIAN NIGHTS COMPRISE 1,001 STORIES *-BUT THE ARCHITECT DID NOT LIKE 2 OF THE STORIES*

SPIRAL CANDLES
LIT BY THE CHINESE ON THEIR TEMPLE ALTARS *BURN FOR 7 DAYS AND 7 NIGHTS*

THE BOY WHO WAS SAVED BY A BEE
AUGUST PFEIFFER (1640-1698)
famed German language expert
BELIEVED KILLED IN A FALL FROM A ROOF AT THE AGE OF 5, WAS ABOUT TO BE BURIED *WHEN A BEE STING CAUSED HIM TO FLUTTER HIS EYELIDS-*
PFEIFFER, UNCONSCIOUS FOR 70 DAYS, VOWED TO LEARN **70 LANGUAGES** *-AND DIED AT THE AGE OF 58- AFTER HE HAD LEARNED HIS 70th LANGUAGE*

WINTER
SPRING AND AUTUMN
SUMMER

THE CHURCH THAT SHOWED THE SEASONS
A WALL, in the Church of St. Sulpice, in Paris, France, HAD AN OPENING THROUGH WHICH SUNLIGHT STREAMED *-STRIKING MARKED SPOTS ON THE FLOOR AND A PILLAR ON THE EXACT DAY ON WHICH EACH OF THE 4 SEASONS STARTED*

1

282 words about the number one

Oliver G. Selfridge

One is an easy number and a hard number. Every number is made up of Ones. Very many things are the One and only things like themselves in the world.

For instance, there is only One of you, and there is only One of me.

It is easy to follow your nose because you have just One. (Where would you put another? Alongside?)

An elephant also has just One trunk.

A plant called bloodroot grows just One leaf and One flower every year. It is very shy and usually lives in deep shade in the forest.

A unicycle has just One wheel, and it is much the hardest kind of cycle to learn to ride, because there are so many different ways to fall off.

There is a saying that One bad apple sours the barrel because the badness can rub off and make the others rotten too. That means that you cannot say that something is perfect if it has One mistake.

The ace, or One, in a deck of cards, is strange because it is sometimes not as strong as a Two and sometimes stronger than all the others.

A talk given by just One person alone is called a monologue or soliloquy, and not a conversation, which takes any number more than One.

Maine is the only state in the United States that touches just One other state.

United States Route One is a road that runs from the most Eastern point of Maine down to the bottom of Florida. It is sometimes called the Post Road, because the mail used to go on it.

The United States is One country. That is what the "united" means.

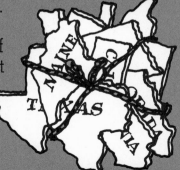

17

Milo and the Mathemagician

Norton Juster

This story is from The Phantom Tollbooth, *a book about a boy named Milo. Milo believes learning is a big waste of time, until he journeys into the treacherous lands beyond the Kingdom of Wisdom. He travels with his friends the Humbug, an uneducated bug who enjoys being ignorant, and Tock, a clockwise dog who ticks. In this episode, Milo and his friends are on their way to Digitopolis when they get sidetracked in the Mathemagician's numbers mine.*

Up ahead the road divided into three and, as if in reply to Milo's question, an enormous road sign, pointing in all three directions, stated clearly:

"Let's travel by miles," advised the Humbug. "It's shorter."

"Let's travel by half inches," suggested Milo. "It's quicker."

"But which road should we take?" asked Tock. "It must make a difference."

As they argued, a most peculiar little figure stepped nimbly from behind the sign and approached them, talking all the while. "Yes, indeed; indeed it does; certainly; my, yes; it does make a difference; undoubtedly."

He was constructed (for that's really the only way to describe him) of a large assortment of lines and angles connected together into one solid many-sided shape—somewhat like a cube that's had all its corners cut off and then had all its corners cut off again. Each of the edges was neatly labeled with a small letter and each of the angles with a large one. He wore a handsome beret on top, and peering intently from one of his several surfaces was a very serious face. Perhaps if you look at the picture you'll know what I mean.

When he reached the car, the figure doffed his cap and recited in a loud clear voice:

My angles are many.
My sides are not few.
I'm the Dodecahedron.
Who are you?

"What's a Dodecahedron?" inquired Milo, who was barely able to pronounce the strange word.

"See for yourself," he said, turning around slowly. "A Dodecahedron is a mathematical shape with twelve faces."

Just as he said it, eleven other faces appeared, one on each surface, and each one wore a different expression.

"I usually use one at a time," he confided, as all but the smiling one disappeared again. "It saves wear and tear. What are you called?"

"Milo," said Milo.

"That is an odd name," he said, changing his smiling face for a frowning one. "And you only have one face."

"Is that bad?" asked Milo, making sure it was still there.

"You'll soon wear it out using it for everything," replied the Dodecahedron. "Now I have one for smiling, one for laughing, one for crying, one for frowning, one for thinking, one for pouting, and six more besides. Is everyone with one face called a Milo?"

"Oh no," Milo replied; "some are called Henry or George or Robert or John or lots of other things."

"How terribly confusing," he cried. "Everything here is called exactly what it is. The triangles are called triangles, the circles are called circles, and even the same numbers have the same name. Why, can you imagine what would happen if we named all the twos Henry or George or Robert or John or lots of other things? You'd have to say Robert plus John equals four, and if the four's name were Albert, things would be hopeless."

"I never thought of it that way," Milo admitted.

"Then I suggest you begin at once," admonished the Dodecahedron from his admonishing face, "for here in Digitopolis everything is quite precise."

"Then perhaps you can help us decide which road to take," said Milo.

"By all means," he replied happily. "There's nothing to it. If a small car carrying three people at thirty miles an hour for ten minutes along a road five miles long at 11:35 in the morning starts at the same time as three people who have been traveling in a little automobile at twenty miles an hour for fifteen minutes on another road exactly twice as long as one half the distance of the other, while a dog, a bug, and a boy travel an equal distance in the same time or the same distance in an equal time along a third road in mid-October, then which one arrives first and which is the best way to go?"

"Seventeen!" shouted the Humbug, scribbling furiously on a piece of paper.

"Well, I'm not sure, but ——" Milo stammered after several minutes of frantic figuring.

"You'll have to do better than that," scolded the Dodecahedron, "or you'll never know how far you've gone or whether or not you've ever gotten there."

"I'm not very good at problems," admitted Milo.

"What a shame," sighed the Dodecahedron. "They're so very useful. Why, did you know that if a beaver two feet long with a tail a foot and a half long can build a dam twelve feet high and six feet wide in two days, all you would need to build Boulder Dam is a beaver sixty-eight feet long with a fifty-one-foot tail?"

"Where would you find a beaver that big?" grumbled the Humbug as his pencil point snapped.

"I'm sure I don't know," he replied, "but if you did, you'd certainly know what to do with him."

"That's absurd," objected Milo, whose head was spinning from all the numbers and questions.

"That may be true," he acknowledged, "but it's completely accurate, and as long as the answer is right, who cares if the question is wrong? If you want sense, you'll have to make it yourself."

"All three roads arrive at the same place at the same time," interrupted Tock, who had patiently been doing the first problem.

"Correct!" shouted the Dodecahedron. "And I'll take you there myself. Now you can see how important problems are. If you hadn't done this one properly, you might have gone the wrong way."

"I can't see where I made my mistake," said the Humbug, frantically rechecking his figures.

"But if all the roads arrive at the same place at the same time, then aren't they all the right way?" asked Milo.

"Certainly not!" he shouted, glaring from his most upset face. "They're all the *wrong* way. Just because you have a choice, it doesn't mean that any of them *has* to be right."

He walked to the sign and quickly spun it around three times. As he did, the three roads vanished and a new one suddenly appeared, heading in the direction that the sign now pointed.

"Is every road five miles from Digitopolis?" asked Milo.

"I'm afraid it has to be," the Dodecahedron replied, leaping onto the back of the car. "It's the only sign we've got."

The new road was quite bumpy and full of stones, and each time they hit one, the Dodecahedron bounced into the air and landed on one of his faces, with a sulk or a smile or a laugh or a frown, depending upon which one it was.

"We'll soon be there," he announced happily, after one of his short flights. "Welcome to the land of numbers."

"It doesn't look very inviting," the bug remarked, for, as they climbed higher and higher, not a tree or a blade of grass could be seen anywhere. Only the rocks remained.

"Is this the place where numbers are made?" asked Milo as the car lurched again, and this time the Dodecahedron sailed off down the mountainside, head over heels and grunt over grimace, until he landed sad side up at what looked like the entrance to a cave.

"They're not made," he replied, as if nothing had happened. "You have to dig for them. Don't you know anything at all about numbers?"

"Well, I don't think they're very important," snapped Milo, too embarrassed to admit the truth.

"NOT IMPORTANT!" roared the Dodecahedron, turning red with fury. "Could you have tea for two without the two—or three blind mice without the three? Would there be four corners of the earth if there weren't a four? And how would you sail the seven seas without a seven?"

"All I mean was ——" began Milo, but the Dodecahedron, overcome with emotion and shouting furiously, carried right on.

"If you had high hopes, how would you know how high they were? And did you know that narrow escapes come in all different widths? Would you travel the whole wide world without ever knowing how wide it was? And how could you do anything at long last," he concluded, waving his arms over his head, "without knowing how long the last was? Why, numbers are the most beautiful and valuable things in the world. Just follow me and I'll show you." He turned on his heel and stalked off into the cave.

"Come along, come along," he shouted from the dark hole. "I can't wait for you all day." And in a moment they'd followed him into the mountain.

It took several minutes for their eyes to become accustomed to the dim light, and during that time strange scratching, scraping, tapping, scuffling noises could be heard all around them.

"Put these on," instructed the Dodecahedron, handing each of them a helmet with a flashlight attached to the top.

"Where are we going?" whispered Milo, for it seemed like the kind of place in which you whispered.

"We're here," he replied with a sweeping gesture. "This is the numbers mine."

Milo squinted into the darkness and saw for the first time that they had entered a vast cavern lit only by a soft, eerie glow from the great stalactites which hung ominously from the ceiling. Passages and corridors honeycombed the walls and wound their way from floor to ceiling, up and down the sides of the cave. And, everywhere he looked, Milo saw little men no bigger than himself busy digging and chopping, shoveling and scraping, pulling and tugging carts full of stone from one place to another.

"Right this way," instructed the Dodecahedron, "and watch where you step."

As he spoke, his voice echoed and re-echoed and re-echoed again, mixing its sound with the buzz of activity all around them. Tock trotted along next to Milo, and the Humbug, stepping daintily, followed behind.

"Whose mine is it?" asked Milo, stepping around two of the loaded wagons.

"BY THE FOUR MILLION EIGHT HUNDRED AND TWENTY-SEVEN THOUSAND SIX HUNDRED AND FIFTY-NINE HAIRS ON MY HEAD, IT'S MINE, OF COURSE!" bellowed a voice from across the cavern. And striding toward them came a figure who could only have been the Mathemagician.

He was dressed in a long flowing robe covered entirely with complex mathematical equations and a tall pointed cap that made him look very wise. In his left hand he carried a long staff with a pencil point at one end and a large rubber eraser at the other.

"It's a lovely mine," apologized the Humbug, who was always intimidated by loud noises.

"The biggest number mine in the kingdom," said the Mathemagician proudly.

"Are there any precious stones in it?" asked Milo excitedly.

"PRECIOUS STONES!" he roared, even louder than before. And then he leaned over toward Milo and whispered softly, "By the eight million two hundred and forty-seven thousand three hundred and twelve threads in my robe, I'll say there are. Look here."

He reached into one of the carts and pulled out a small object, which he polished vigorously on his robe. When he held it up to the light, it sparkled brightly.

"But that's a five," objected Milo, for that was certainly what it was.

"Exactly," agreed the Mathemagician; "as valuable a jewel as you'll find anywhere. Look at some of the others."

He scooped up a great handful of stones and poured them into Milo's arms. They included all the numbers from one to nine, and even an assortment of zeros.

"We dig them and polish them right here," volunteered the Dodecahedron, pointing to a group of workers busily employed at the buffing wheels; "and then we send them all over the world. Marvelous, aren't they?"

"They are exceptional," said Tock, who had a special fondness for numbers.

"So that's where they come from," said Milo, looking in awe at the glittering collection of numbers. He returned them to the Dodecahedron as carefully as possible but, as he did, one dropped to the floor with a smash and broke in two. The Humbug winced and Milo looked terribly concerned.

"Oh, don't worry about that," said the Mathemagician as he scooped up the pieces. "We use the broken ones for fractions."

"Haven't you any diamonds or emeralds or rubies?" asked the bug irritably, for he was quite disappointed in what he'd seen so far.

"Yes, indeed," the Mathemagician replied, leading them to the rear of the cave; "right this way."

There, piled into enormous mounds that reached almost to the ceiling, were not only diamonds and emeralds and rubies but also sapphires, amethysts, topazes, moonstones, and garnets. It was the most amazing mass of wealth that any of them had ever seen.

"They're such a terrible nuisance," sighed the Mathemagician, "and no one can think of what to do with them. So we just keep digging them up and throwing them out. Now," he said, taking a silver whistle from his pocket and blowing it loudly, "let's have some lunch."

And for the first time in his life the astonished bug couldn't think of a thing to say.

Into the cavern rushed eight of the strongest miners carrying an immense caldron which bubbled and sizzled and sent great clouds of savory steam spiraling slowly to the ceiling. A sweet yet pungent aroma hung in the air and drifted easily from one anxious nose to the other, stopping only long enough to make several mouths water and a few stomachs growl. Milo, Tock, and the Humbug watched eagerly as the rest of the workers put down their tools and gathered around the big pot to help themselves.

"Perhaps you'd care for something to eat?" said the Mathemagician, offering each of them a heaping bowlful.

"Yes, sir," said Milo, who was beside himself with hunger.

"Thank you," added Tock.

The Humbug made no reply, for he was already too busy eating, and in a moment the three of them had finished absolutely everything they'd been given.

"Please have another portion," said the Mathemagician, filling their bowls once more; and as quickly as they'd finished the first one the second was emptied too.

"Don't stop now," he insisted, serving them again,
        and again,
                and again,
                        and again,
                                and again.

"How very strange," thought Milo as he finished his seventh helping. "Each one I eat makes me a little hungrier than the one before.

"Do have some more," suggested the Mathemagician, and they continued to eat just as fast as he filled the plates.

After Milo had eaten nine portions, Tock eleven, and the Hum-

bug, without once stopping to look up, twenty-three, the Mathemagician blew his whistle for a second time and immediately the pot was removed and the miners returned to work.

"U-g-g-g-h-h-h," gasped the bug, suddenly realizing that he was twenty-three times hungrier than when he started, "I think I'm starving."

"Me, too," complained Milo, whose stomach felt as empty as he could ever remember; "and I ate so much."

"Yes, it was delicious, wasn't it?" agreed the pleased Dodecahedron, wiping the gravy from several of his mouths. "It's the speciality of the kingdom—subtraction stew."

"I have more of an appetite than when I began," said Tock, leaning weakly against one of the larger rocks.

"Certainly," replied the Mathemagician; "what did you expect? The more you eat, the hungrier you get. Everyone knows that."

"They do?" said Milo doubtfully. "Then how do you ever get enough?"

"Enough?" he said impatiently. "Here in Digitopolis we have our meals when we're full and eat until we're hungry. That way, when you don't have anything at all, you have more than enough. It's a very economical system. You must have been quite stuffed to have eaten so much."

"It's completely logical," explained the Dodecahedron. "The

more you want, the less you get, and the less you get, the more you have. Simple arithmetic, that's all. Suppose you had something and added something to it. What would that make?"

"More," said Milo quickly.

"Quite correct," he nodded. "Now suppose you had something and added nothing to it. What would you have?"

"The same," he answered again, without much conviction.

"Splendid," cried the Dodecahedron. "And suppose you had something and added less than nothing to it. What would you have then?"

"FAMINE!" roared the anguished Humbug, who suddenly realized that that was exactly what he'd eaten twenty-three bowls of.

"It's not as bad as all that," said the Dodecahedron from his most sympathetic face. "In a few hours you'll be nice and full again —just in time for dinner."

"Oh dear," said Milo sadly and softly. "I only eat when I'm hungry."

"What a curious idea," said the Mathemagician, raising his staff over his head and scrubbing the rubber end back and forth several times on the ceiling. "The next thing you'll have us believe is that you only sleep when you're tired." And by the time he'd finished the sentence, the cavern, the miners, and the Dodecahedron had vanished, leaving just the four of them standing in the Mathemagician's workshop.

"I often find," he casually explained to his dazed visitors, "that the best way to get from one place to another is to erase everything and begin again. Please make yourself at home."

"Do you always travel that way?" asked Milo as he glanced curiously at the strange circular room, whose sixteen tiny arched windows corresponded exactly to the sixteen points of the compass. Around the entire circumference were numbers from zero to three hundred and sixty, marking the degrees of the circle, and on the floor, walls, tables, chairs, desks, cabinets, and ceiling were labels showing their heights, widths, depths, and distances to and from each other. To one side was a gigantic note pad set on an artist's easel, and from hooks and strings hung a collection of scales, rulers, measures, weights, tapes, and all sorts of other devices for measuring any number of things in every possible way.

"No indeed," replied the Mathemagician, and this time he raised the sharpened end of his staff, drew a thin straight line in the air, and then walked gracefully across it from one side of the room to the other. "Most of the time I take the shortest distance between any two points. And, of course, when I should be in several places at once," he remarked, writing $7 \times 1 = 7$ carefully on the note pad, "I simply multiply."

Suddenly there were seven Mathemagicians standing side by side, and each one looked exactly like the other.

"How did you do that?" gasped Milo.

"There's nothing to it," they all said in chorus, "if you have a magic staff." Then six of them canceled themselves out and simply disappeared.

"But it's only a big pencil," the Humbug objected, tapping at it with his cane.

"True enough," agreed the Mathemagician; "but once you learn to use it, there's no end to what you can do."

"Can you make things disappear?" asked Milo excitedly.

"Why, certainly," he said, striding over to the easel. "Just step a little closer and watch carefully."

After demonstrating that there was nothing up his sleeves, in his hat, or behind his back, he wrote quickly:

$$4+9-2\times16+1\div3\times6-67+8\times2-3+26-$$
$$1\div34+3\div7+2-5=$$

Then he looked up expectantly.

"Seventeen!" shouted the bug, who always managed to be first with the wrong answer.

"It all comes to zero," corrected Milo.

"Precisely," said the Mathemagician, making a very theatrical bow, and the entire line of numbers vanished before their eyes. "Now is there anything else you'd like to see?"

"Yes, please," said Milo. "Can you show me the biggest number there is?"

"I'd be delighted," he replied, opening one of the closet doors. "We keep it right here. It took four miners just to dig it out."

Inside was the biggest  Milo had ever seen.

It was fully twice as high as the Mathemagician.

"No, that's not what I mean," objected Milo. "Can you show me the longest number there is?"

"Surely," said the Mathemagician, opening another door. "Here it is. It took three carts to carry it here."

Inside this closet was the longest imaginable. It was just about as wide as the three was high.

"No, no, no, that's not what I mean either," he said, looking helplessly at Tock.

"I think what you would like to see," said the dog, scratching himself just under half-past four, "is the number of greatest possible magnitude."

"Well, why didn't you say so?" said the Mathemagician, who was busily measuring the edge of a raindrop. "What's the greatest number *you* can think of?"

"Nine trillion, nine hundred ninety-nine billion, nine hundred ninety-nine million, nine hundred ninety-nine thousand, nine hundred ninety-nine," recited Milo breathlessly.

"Very good," said the Mathemagician. "Now add one to it. Now add one again," he repeated when Milo had added the previous one. "Now add one again. Now add one again. Now add one again. Now add one again. Now add one again. Now add one again. Now add ——"

"But when can I stop?" pleaded Milo.

"Never," said the Mathemagician with a little smile, "for the number you want is always at least one more than the number you've got, and it's so large that if you started saying it yesterday you wouldn't finish tomorrow."

"Where could you ever find a number so big?" scoffed the Humbug.

"In the same place they have the smallest number there is," he answered helpfully; "and you know what that is."

"Certainly," said the bug, suddenly remembering something to do at the other end of the room.

"One one-millionth?" asked Milo, trying to think of the smallest fraction possible.

"Almost," said the Mathemagician. "Now divide it in half. Now divide it in half again. Now divide it in half again. Now divide it in half again. Now divide it in half again. Now divide it in half again. Now divide ———"

"Oh dear," shouted Milo, holding his hands to his ears, "doesn't that ever stop either?"

"How can it," said the Mathemagician, "when you can always take half of whatever you have left until it's so small that if you started to say it right now you'd finish even before you began?"

"Where could you keep anything so tiny?" Milo asked, trying very hard to imagine such a thing.

The Mathemagician stopped what he was doing and explained simply, "Why, in a box that's so small you can't see it —— and that's kept in a drawer that's so small you can't see it, in a dresser that's so small you can't see it, in a house that's so small you can't see it, on a street that's so small you can't see it, in a city that's so small you can't see it, which is part of a country that's so small you can't see it, in a world that's so small you can't see it."

Then he sat down, fanned himself with a handkerchief, and continued. "Then, of course, we keep the whole thing in another box that's so small you can't see it—and, if you follow me, I'll show you where to find it."

They walked to one of the small windows and there, tied to the sill, was one end of a line that stretched along the ground and into the distance until completely out of sight.

"Just follow that line forever," said the Mathemagician, "and when you reach the end, turn left. There you'll find the land of Infinity, where the tallest, the shortest, the biggest, the smallest, and the most and the least of everything are kept."

"I really don't have that much time," said Milo anxiously. "Isn't there a quicker way?"

"Well, you might try this flight of stairs," he suggested, opening another door and pointing up. "It goes there, too."

Milo bounded across the room and started up the stairs two at a time. "Wait for me, please," he shouted to Tock and the Humbug. "I'll be gone just a few minutes."

Up he went—very quickly at first—then more slowly—then in a little while even more slowly than that—and finally, after many minutes of climbing up the endless stairway, one weary foot was barely able to follow the other. Milo suddenly realized that with all his effort he was no closer to the top than when he began, and not a great deal further from the bottom. But he struggled on for a while longer, until at last, completely exhausted, he collapsed onto one of the steps.

"I should have known it," he mumbled, resting his tired legs and filling his lungs with air. "This is just like the line that goes on forever, and I'll never get there."

"You wouldn't like it much anyway," someone replied gently. "Infinity is a dreadfully poor place. They can never manage to make ends meet."

"Someone" turned out to be a boy who was divided neatly in half from his head to his feet. To find out what the little half-boy had to say about averages, and to learn more about Milo's adventures in the Lands Beyond, look for "The Phantom Tollbooth" in your library.

Bird Words

Each of these 5 <u>mathematical sentences</u> gives the name of a common bird. To find it, write out the name for each picture in the sentence, then add or subtract words or letters according to the math signs between pictures.

1 $-$ $+$ $= ?$

2 $-$ $+$ $+$ $-$ BEEF $= ?$

3 🧩 − 🂡 + 🛶 = **?**

4 { 🐷 + ⬜ − 🍳 + 🐝 + *TON* − 🌰 = **?** }

5 ☆ + 🌳 + 🧑 − 🌲🌲🌲 = **?**

43

YOU CAN CHECK YOUR BIRD WORDS ON PAGE 64.

Captured by Qaptain Qidd

Victor E. Hass

This is a chapter from a book called The Magic Numerals of Ali Khayyam. *Ali Khayyam, who really likes to be called Al, thought he was very lucky when he won first prize in the Crunchy-Munchie slogan contest. He got a chance to be on TV, plus he won the grand prize of $100,-000. However, Al found out that the only way he could*

collect his prize was to spend half of it on a round-the-world trip. That turned out to be difficult, because everywhere Al went, people counted a different way. In a country called Arcadia, the first place he visited, people counted by 5's. Other places people counted by 12 or 2—or anything else except 10, which is the way Al, and everyone else in America, counted. So he had trouble keeping track of how much of his prize money he spent, and how much he had left.

Then one day, Al got lost at sea and ended up on the island of a not-so-ferocious one-eyed giant called Cyclops. Cyclops, who counted by 2's, captured Al and wouldn't let him escape because he thought Al might tell people the truth. The truth was—Cyclops was really a nice giant. If Al told anyone, it would certainly ruin Cyclops' reputation as a mean, one-eyed monster. So Cyclops held Al prisoner on the beach. Al got very sad because he knew he would never spend the $50,000 he had left if he couldn't leave Cyclops' island. Then something strange happened . . .

Al sat down and kicked the sand dejectedly. A big lump gathered in his throat, and he could hear his heart beat.

Thump, thump, thump.

45

Al jumped up excitedly! That wasn't his heart at all. It sounded like someone digging in the sand. He crawled cautiously to the top of the sand dune to see what was going on. On the other side, at the shore, he saw a longboat drawn up on the beach. Farther up the beach Al saw a group of men digging a deep hole at the base of a palm tree. They had several large oaken chests near their feet.

Cyclops was right. They were pirates. They were here to bury their treasure.

"This is it!" Al whispered to himself. "Cyclops is on the other side of the island. I can escape."

He jumped to his feet and ran toward the men. "Hey!" he yelled excitedly, "I'm Ali Khayyam. Take me with you."

"Caramba! Supristo! Gringo! Diablo!" screamed the largest pirate in anger. "Who is the dog of a scoundrel who interrupts us?" The man was livid with rage.

"Off with his head!" he screamed, whipping out his cutlass.

Then they all heard a crashing noise crossing the island.

"Quick! It's Cyclops!" one of the men howled.

They grabbed the treasure chests and ran to the longboat. One of the pirates picked Al up and tucked him under his arm as he ran.

"We will take you for a hostage," he yelled.

They jumped into the longboat, after throwing in their treasure chests. Each man scrambled and clawed his way into the boat. The last man shoved the boat off the sand, and then jumped in, grabbing an oar with the rest.

They all rowed madly toward their ship, a huge galleon with a large pirate's flag at the mast.

At that moment Cyclops charged over the last sand dune and saw them. He roared and howled and shook his fist at Al. As the pirates approached the ship, Cyclops screamed desperately to Al.

"Don't you dare tell!"

"I won't," Al yelled back to him.

When Cyclops heard this he slowly winked his eye and stopped his horrible noise for a moment. Then he bellowed louder, and started throwing coconuts at the longboat.

"He is throwing skulls at us!" screamed one of the sailors, in a frenzy.

On hearing this the men rowed even faster. They were going so fast that they churned up a gigantic rooster-tail behind the longboat.

"Just like Slo-Mo-IV, the famous hydroplane," thought Al, as they neared the pirate ship. When they reached the side of the galleon, one of the pirates carried Al up the rope ladder at the side of the ship, and set him on the deck. The rest of the swarthy crew carried the treasure chests up and dropped them on the deck.

They fell with a rending clatter and broke open, spilling coins in every direction.

The largest pirate, who was the captain, came on deck last, and looked in consternation at the mess.

"Money, money, money! All over my nice clean ship," he howled. "Someone will pay for this, just as sure as my name is Qaptain Qidd."

The first mate bounded quickly forward. "Sir, it's that young rapscallion's fault. We had found a perfect hiding place on the Island of Cyclops when this boy woke the monster and we had to flee."

The first mate shook his finger in Al's face. "If it hadn't been for you, young man, we would have been successful."

The captain roared, "String him up to the yard arm! Throw him into the brig! Make him walk the plank!"

Three sailors jumped forward and grabbed Al, pulling him in three directions at once.

Now it was Al's turn to howl. "Let go of me!" he yelled. "You're hurting me!"

The sailors jumped back in dismay. "Sorry," they said, "we didn't mean to."

The first mate raised his hand. "Sir," he said, "may I suggest something?"

"What is it, mate?" the captain barked.

"Qaptain Qidd, sir, why don't we make this whippersnapper clean up the money on the deck? He can put it into bundles, and put it back into the chests. After that we can hang him."

"An excellent idea!" declared the captain.

"Hurrah!" shouted the crew. They were in favor of the suggestion because they would not have to do the work themselves.

"Put the young whelp to work, and get the crew into the rigging, mate. We must sail at once."

"Aye, aye, sir," the mate saluted the captain.

"NOW HEAR THIS! NOW HEAR THIS!" he roared at the crew. "All hands on deck! Avast and belay! Man the rigging! Qap-Qidd expects every man to do his duty."

The crew scurried aloft and soon the wind was filling the sails of the galleon, as they sailed away from Cyclops' island.

"Everything is A-O.K., sir," the mate reported to the captain.

"Good," the latter muttered, as he clumped off to his cabin.

The mate turned and smiled sweetly at Al. "Now, young man, we may as well be polite to each other in the few short days you have left."

"What do you mean?" gasped Al.

"Well, of course, as soon as you have finished counting the money, we will have to feed you to the sharks. But in the meantime we may as well be friends."

The mate drew up a keg of gunpowder and sat down by Al. "My name is Aye Habb," he said. "My ancestors came from Arabia, but I was born and raised in Soho, London."

"Aha!" exclaimed Al. "My name is Ali Khayyam, and my

ancestors came from Arabia. But I am a Californian."

"Not *the* Ali Khayyam?" exclaimed Aye Habb. "The television celebrity."

"Yes," said Al modestly.

"This certainly changes things, young man. I'll tell Qaptain Qidd about this. Perhaps he will let you live a little longer."

"A little longer!" exclaimed Al in dismay. "Why don't you tell the captain to hold me for ransom?"

The mate thought a moment. "Not a bad idea at that. I'll speak to Qaptain Qidd about it. But, in the meantime, you have a big job ahead of you. You have to sort out all the money that was spilled on the deck. We must get it all counted and figured and back into the chests."

Al started to pick up bagfuls of coins that lay scattered all over the deck, in the gunwales and scuppers, and everywhere else, it seemed.

The mate brought him a pencil and some paper.

"What is that for?" Al asked.

"You must keep track of how much you have collected. We must have an accurate inventory, you know."

Al sighed and took the pencil and paper. "How shall I record these?" he asked.

"How many pieces of eight do you have in that bag?"

Al opened the bag. "Pieces of eight?"

"Of course! What else do pirates collect?"

"I guess you are right," admitted Al. "But you could have Spanish doubloons."

"We do! We do! But you will get to those later. Now, how many pieces of eight do you have?"

Al counted the coins in the first bag. "One hundred and thirteen pieces of eight."

"How much money is that?"

"Nine hundred and four dollars."

Al started to write it down.

"Wait a moment," Aye Habb stopped him. "You realize, of course, that since we are counting pieces of eight, we must do so in base eight?"

"Oh," exclaimed Al, "I think I know how to do that. $904 is—" Al hesitated, then wrote on his paper:

$$B^4 \quad B^3 \quad B^2 \quad B^1 \quad B^0$$
$$(4096) \quad (512) \quad (64) \quad (8) \quad (1)$$

"Now, let's see," Al mused. "I know 512 will divide into 904 once, with a remainder of 392, and 64 will divide into 392 six times, with a remainder of 8. And 8, of course, is contained in 8 once."

When he was finished, his work looked like this:

$$512 \overline{)904} \, 1$$
$$\underline{512}$$
$$64 \overline{)392} \, 6$$
$$\underline{384}$$
$$8 \overline{)8} \, 1$$
$$\underline{8}$$
$$0$$

$$B^5 \quad B^3 \quad B^2 \quad B^1 \quad U$$
$$(4096) \quad (512) \quad (64) \quad (8) \quad (1)$$
$$\qquad\quad 1 \qquad\quad 6 \qquad\quad 1$$

"We have 161 pieces of eight in this sack," he told Aye Habb.

The mate looked at Al scornfully. "If that is the best you can do, we had better toss you to the sharks right now," he said derisively. "How many ones have you?"

Al looked at his figures in dismay.

Aye Habb took the pencil and wrote a zero under home plate and added the symbol for "pieces of eight" so that the numeral now looked like this: $1610. "We have 1 base cubed, 6 bases squared, 1 base, and *no* ones," the mate said with a flourish. "There is quite a difference, you know."

Al felt rather sheepish. "I left out the zero."

I LEFT OUT THE ZERO

"Leaving out the zero can be disastrous," the mate said.

"But how can the bags have any ones in them if they are all pieces of eight?" asked Al.

"Some of the coins are mixed," Aye Habb admitted. He picked up a bag marked, "$2013." "How much is this in base eight?"

Al's figures looked like this:

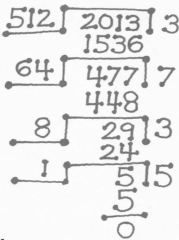

$$512 \overline{) 2013 } \, 3$$
$$1536$$
$$64 \overline{) 477 } \, 7$$
$$448$$
$$8 \overline{) 29 } \, 3$$
$$24$$
$$1 \overline{) 5 } \, 5$$
$$5$$
$$0$$

"83735," Al told Aye Habb.

"Right! That's a lot better. Here is a large pile of bags containing pieces of eight. Figure these," Aye Habb said.

While Al was gathering up the treasure trove, the mate went below to talk to Qaptain Qidd. Al could hear the captain's blustering roar and the clumping of his wooden leg as he stomped about. The boy tried hard to understand what was being said, but the wind made too much noise as it whistled through the sails.

One of the deck hands came to talk to Al. "My name is Longjon Argentum," he told Al.

"And mine is Ali Khayyam," Al said politely.

"Yes, I know," the sailor said eagerly. "The news is all over the ship. We are really very flattered to have you aboard. Tell me, how did you manage to escape from Cyclops?"

Al told him part of the story—not all of it, of course because he had promised Cyclops that he would not tell the part about the make-believe bones, and the part about Cyclops' being a vegetarian.

The other sailors had gathered around Al to hear what he had to say.

"But, tell me," Al asked Longjon, "how is it that you came back to Cyclops' island to bury your treasure?"

"Oh, we do that all the time," Longjon said. "We sail into his main bay and attract his attention. This throws him off guard. Then at night we sail around to the other side, and bury our treasure. We figure that that is the safest place in the world to hide it. No one would ever dare search for it there."

"You have a point there," Al said admiringly. "Do you think the captain will decide to ransom me?"

"No doubt about it," Longjon said. "A famous boy like you? I should say so! By the way, would you give me your autograph?"

"Yes, of course," Al agreed. He was flattered.

"Me, too! Me, too!" the other sailors chorused. Al used almost all of his paper signing autographs for the pirates.

"I think it would be only fair if you all gave me your autographs," Al said politely.

"He is right," Longjon agreed. "What do we have that is big enough for all of us to write on?"

"Here is something," one of the crew said. He took a large sheet of parchment out of his jacket, and after unfolding it, placed it on the deck. It was covered with lines, so he turned it over to the blank side. The sailors all gathered round and signed their names on it. Some of them just wrote X because they had never learned to wrote. Longjon folded the parchment and handed it to Al.

Just then they heard the captain clumping his way to the top deck. The pirates all scurried off to their jobs. Al put the large sheet of folded parchment into his pocket, and turned back to his job of counting money.

Qaptain Qidd and Aye Habb came out on deck and approached Al. The captain was smiling and seemed to be an altogether different man.

"Well, well, well," he wheezed, rubbing his hands together,

"so you're the young Mr. Khayyam! I saw you on television when we were in port last. How are you enjoying your stay aboard?"

Al looked at him in surprise. "I'm not quite through with the money, sir."

"Not through with the money?" the captain asked sweetly. He turned to Longjon, who was working nearby.

"LONGJON!" he bellowed in a ferocious roar. "Get over here and help the young man. Do we want him to become tired from counting? NO, WE DON'T!" he thundered. Then he turned to Al and smiled.

"If there is anything we can do to make you comfortable, let me know." Then he looked at the mate.

"Aye Habb!"

The mate saluted smartly. "Yes, sir, Qaptain Qidd, sir?"

"See that our guest is well cared for." The captain turned and went below.

"Whew!" Al whistled. "I never saw such a change before."

"Money talks," the mate said, winking. "We decided to hold you for fifty thousand dollars ransom."

"Why don't you make it one hundred thousand dollars?" asked Al. "I've got that much in a bank in Arcadia."

"Dollars or quinteros?" asked Aye Habb.

"Dollars," Al told him ruefully. Then he told the mate how the Revoluting Party had almost ruined him by making him rich.

58

"I don't know how I can get rid of it all." He sighed.

Aye Habb laughed gleefully. "We will help you," he promised.

Al escaped from Qaptain Qidd before the pirates could spend any of his money. However, they recaptured him because the piece of parchment he took turned out to be a treasure map. If you want to find out if Al ever did manage to win his prize, look in your library for The Magic Numerals of Ali Khayyam.

Fun with Palindromes

Palindromes are words or sentences that are the same when read backward or forward. The picture shows how Adam, when he first met Eve, might have introduced himself by speaking a palindrome, and how Eve might have replied by speaking another. Even the serpent is uttering a palindrome!

There are hundreds of longer sentences that read the same both ways. Here are a few clever ones:

A MAN, A PLAN, A CANAL—PANAMA!
WAS IT A BAR OR A BAT I SAW?
DRAW PUPIL'S LIP UPWARD
TEN ANIMALS I SLAM IN A NET
POOR DAN IS IN A DROOP
NO, IT IS OPEN ON ONE POSITION
NAME NO ONE MAN
ABLE WAS I ERE I SAW ELBA

How good are you at recognizing a palindromic word when you come across one in your reading? To test yourself, see how many such words you can find in the following paragraphs:

"Look at the sun, over there behind that radar tower," said Hannah. "I think it looks much redder that it did at noon."

"Wow! It sure does, Ma'am," exclaimed Otto, bending over to pat the head of a small brown pup with black markings over one eye.

Piet Hein,
Mathematician, Designer, Poet

The man who wrote the poems on the next page doesn't call them poems, and he isn't just a poet. His name is Piet Hein. He calls his poems "grooks" which is a name he just made up one day. Besides being a poet, he is a designer, painter, engineer, writer, and mathematician. He designed all the geometric shapes on this page.

    Piet Hein's most famous shape is the super-elipse. He invented it when he was working on a traffic problem in Stockholm, Sweden. He needed to design a street intersection in a space that was too small to be a square and too big to be a circle. So he designed the super-ellipse. It's a shape in between a square and a circle, or a rectangle and an ellipse. Now the shape is so famous that it can be seen in tables, plates, lampshades, carpets, curtains, and so on. Other shapes he has invented are the super-circle, the tri-super-ellipse, and the super-egg, a 3-D shape you get when you spin a super-ellipse like a top. He also created a puzzle called the soma cube, which is made up of the seven pieces scattered across the bottom of this page. Can you figure out how to put it together?

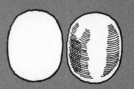
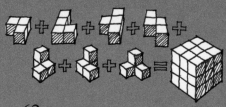